Math in the Mall

by Margaret Thomas

illustrated by Milton Hall

cover design: Jeff Van Kanegan

Cover Photo Courtesy of Mall of America
Minneapolis, Minnesota

Publisher
Instructional Fair • TS Denison
Grand Rapids, Michigan 49544

ISBN: 1-56822-845-7

Math in the Mall

Copyright © 1999 by Ideal • Instructional Fair Publishing Group
a division of Tribune Education
2400 Turner Avenue NW
Grand Rapids, Michigan 49544

TABLE OF CONTENTS

ABOUT THE BOOK

Math in the Mall provides information for teachers to use to develop class activities using a shopping mall as a learning environment for mathematical investigations. The book includes four sections: *Teacher Plans, Suggested Activities/Projects, Mall Math,* and *Other Math Field Trips.* The *Teacher Plans* section includes checklists, cooperative learning group information, home letters, reporting forms, and assessments. The *Suggested Activities/Projects* section contains blackline copy masters of field trip and project activities. The *Mall Math* section contains activities that review math concepts that students may use when they actually visit the mall. Included are geometric terms, ratios, percent, units conversion, and data analysis. *Other Math Field Trips* section offers additional information and activities to use in a museum or an amusement park.

The materials included provide step-by-step time lines for planning and implementing the project suggestions. Information is given concerning group and individual activities with emphasis on cooperative learning techniques. Communications to parents are also included. Project guidelines, such as stating the problem, identifying needed materials and procedures, collecting data, drawing conclusions, making revisions, and completing extensions are given in template form for class discussions and student assignments. Assessment suggestions include tips for completing a project, a scoring rubric system, and self-assessment forms.

Teachers are encouraged to adapt the materials to meet their own teaching styles. The project activities can be used in a variety of shopping mall situations. Many activities can be used in other locations as well. Several items can be used as transparency masters for class discussions.

Throughout the activities, teachers and students are asked to see and use mathematics to investigate various environments.

Teacher Plans

The *Teacher Plans* section provides all the information needed to plan a math field trip to a shopping mall or to assign and assess mathematics projects based on a mall environment. Several pages can be used as transparency copymasters for class discussions or as blackline copymasters for distribution to students or parents.

Teachers should make any necessary changes to meet their own teaching styles, students' learning styles, and school requirements.

Checklists—Math in the Mall Field Trip Checklist—time lines for weeks before the activity, week of the activity, day of the activity, and follow-up

Math in the Mall Project Checklist—step-by-step procedures for preparing students to complete math projects based in a shopping mall environment

Cooperative Learning Groups—information concerning cooperative learning, the formation of groups, problems, and assessment

Field Trip Letter—information to parents and permission slip

Math in the Mall Letter—information to parents

Math in the Mall Report—templates for students to record team members, activities, materials, explanations, plans, solutions/conclusions, revisions, extensions

Scoring Rubrics—Top Ten Tips for Completing a Project
    Project Scoring Rubric
    Student Self-Assessment
    Group Self-Assessment

MATH IN THE MALL FIELD TRIP CHECKLISTS

A *Math in the Mall Field Trip Checklist* and a *Math in the Mall Project Checklist* are included. The activities can be part of a class field trip to a mall or assigned as individual or group projects to be completed outside of class. The checklists and related sheets can also be adapted to museum or amusement park sites.

✎ **SEVERAL WEEKS PRIOR TO THE FIELD TRIP:**

_____ Visit the mall and identify a location that will serve as a base of operation where
  • students will meet to receive any final instructions.

  • students will be able to obtain assistance.

  • students will meet at the conclusion of the field trip.

_____ Determine the time needed or available for the field trip: morning, afternoon, or all day.

_____ Walk through the location to verify
  • that the site will allow for the exploration of mathematical concepts.

  • that assigned activities are appropriate for the site. Refer to the *Suggested Activities/Projects* section. For example, be certain the mall has a food court if food court activities are to be included.

  NOTE: It is not necessary for the teacher to perform the actual activities to have exact answers. Emphasis should be on the methods used and the conclusions made, not on the calculation of "one right answer."

  • the location of restrooms and information/customer service counters.

_____ Contact mall personnel.
- Discuss the planned field trip including the number of students and chaperones and the field trip guidelines.

- Check the date to avoid conflicts, such as construction projects, late mall opening times, or other major events.

- Find out whether the mall offers any special information packets, discounts, or coupons for groups.

_____ Complete school/district paperwork.
- Complete forms required for field trips.

- Request transportation.

- Request chaperones: teachers, parents, assistants.

_____ Review math concepts needed to complete the activities—refer to the _Mall Math_ section.

_____ Outline assessment criteria.
- Inform students of what will be expected prior to the beginning of the activity.

- Refer to the _Scoring Rubrics_ information.

- Refer to the _Student/Group Self-Assessments_.

_____ Send home a notice concerning the field trip.
- Refer to the sample _Field Trip Letter_.

- Explain the math concepts to be explored and the educational activities included.

- List needed materials: calculators, tape measures, string, protractors, etc.

- State any costs: lunch money, spending money, etc.

✎ WEEK OF THE FIELD TRIP:

____ Collect extra materials for the activities:
- measurement tools: tape measures, rulers, string

- stop watches

- protractors, straws

- calculators, paper, pencils

- extra copy of the activities

____ Contact the mall.
- Confirm the date and times to avoid last minute conflicts, such as closed stores, construction, etc.

____ Contact chaperones to confirm times and responsibilities.

____ Assign students to groups of two or more.
- Refer to the *Cooperative Learning Groups* comments.

____ Distribute activity lists.
- Refer to the *Suggested Activities/Projects* section.

- Have groups select their activities or assign the activities.

NOTE: Different groups should have different sets of activities. Students will benefit from observing how different groups solve different problems. Also, assigning different activities prevents the students from moving through the mall as one large group. Some activities could be assigned to more than one group so that students can observe how different strategies are used to solve similar problems.

- Make certain there are enough activities to occupy the time allotted. Students should not "roam the mall."

- Give students specific information concerning time for shopping. Time to shop might be included in a lunch break.

_____ Provide class time for groups to develop a plan (strategies) for their activities.
- Have students list the math tools and materials needed to complete their investigations.

- Encourage each group to assign duties to the members of the group so that all members will be actively involved in the investigations.

_____ Send reminders home.

✎ DAY OF THE FIELD TRIP:

_____ Make certain all necessary forms have been completed.

_____ Announce the location of the base of operation at the mall.

_____ Review safety and behavior rules.
- Emphasize common sense. For example, students should estimate measurements when taking exact measurements would require them to cross barriers or enter restricted areas.

- Require students to stay with their partners or groups at all times.

- Remind students to be very careful when in the parking areas.

- Remind students of safety rules pertaining to escalators and elevators.

_____ Remind the students of the time schedule.
- Announce the time and place to meet at the mall.

- Announce the time for lunch, shopping, etc.

_____ Distribute reporting forms.
- Refer to the *Math in the Mall Report* sheet.

- Adapt the sheet to reflect the number of activities assigned to each group.

✎ AFTER THE FIELD TRIP:

_____ Have the groups complete their reports of their activities.
- The reports should include team members, activities, a plan, results, conclusions, and additional observations.

- The observations should include revisions to their initial plan if the activities were to be repeated and suggestions for additional activities or extensions.

_____ Have the groups present their solutions to the class.
- If more than one group completed a set of activities, use any different approaches and outcomes as a topic for discussion.

- Have students state each member's participation in the activities.

_____ Have students write letters of appreciation to the mall personnel and chaperones.

MATH IN THE MALL PROJECT CHECKLIST

NOTE: Most of the *Checklist* activities should be completed several weeks prior to the project due date. Review of math concepts should continue until the week the projects are due. The *Checklist* contains suggested items and should be adapted to meet teacher and school requirements.

_____ List the various malls in your area where students might complete some of the project activities.

_____ Visit several of the locations.
  • Ensure that the sites will allow for the exploration of the mathematical concepts.

  • Ensure that assigned activities are appropriate for the sites.

NOTE: It is not necessary for the teacher to perform the actual activities to have exact answers. Emphasis should be on the methods used and the conclusions made, not on the calculation of "one right answer."

  • Refer to the *Suggested Activities/Projects* section.

_____ Assign students to groups of two or more.
  • Refer to the *Cooperative Learning Groups* comments in this publication.

  • Present the project topics to the class.

  • Discuss the importance of explaining the methods used to complete the activities. Students need to interpret and analyze their results.

  • Have groups select their project topic or assign the project topics.

_____ Outline assessment criteria.
   - Define for students what is expected prior to the start of the projects and give due dates.

   - Refer to the *Scoring Rubrics* information. Adapt the suggested rubric to your requirements. Explain the major components of the project. Encourage students to be creative in their plans.

   - Refer to the *Student/Group Self-Assessments*.

_____ Send project information home.
   - Include the list of suggested sites.

   - Refer to the *Math in the Mall Letter*.

   - Explain the math concepts to be explored and the educational activities included.

   - Include a suggested time line and project due date.

_____ Review math concepts needed to complete the activities.
   - Refer to the *Mall Math* section.

   - Review a wide range of math concepts in the classroom prior to the project due date.

_____ Distribute reporting forms.
   - Refer to the sample *Math in the Mall Report* sheets.

_____ Provide class time for the groups to develop a plan (strategies) for their project.
   - Have students list steps to complete the project.

   - Have students rank the steps in the order they need to be completed.

- Have students develop a time line and set deadlines for completion of the various tasks.

- Have students list needed math tools and materials.

- Have groups assign duties to each member of the group so that all members will be actively involved in the investigations.

_____ Review safety and behavior rules.
- Emphasize common sense. For example, students should estimate measurements when taking exact measurements would require them to cross barriers or enter restricted areas.

- Require students to stay with their partners or groups at all times.

- Remind students to be very careful when in the parking areas.

- Remind students of safety rules pertaining to escalators and elevators.

COOPERATIVE LEARNING GROUPS

Cooperative learning groups can provide success for students of all ability levels. Groups can often solve problems that individual students might not attempt because the problems may seem too difficult or too time-consuming. Cooperative learning group activities foster the teamwork, social interactions, communication, critical thinking, and problem-solving skills essential for tomorrow's workforce.

A cooperative learning group is not merely a team of students given a problem to solve. Students in a team setting may each solve the problem, compare answers, and choose the best solution for the "team result." A cooperative learning group is an interactive group in which the members have specific responsibilities for completing a task as a team. For cooperative learning to be effective, the members of a cooperative learning group must know what is expected.

Cooperative Learning Groups:

- Members work as a team to complete a task or to solve a specific problem.

- Each member has a role in the solution of the problem, such as recorder, brainstormer, facilitator, and organizer. The roles may be assigned or chosen. Often the roles will change during the solution of the problem.

- Members interact with one another to determine a strategy to solve the problem.

- Each member is responsible for solving the problem and must contribute to the success of the team.

- Each member is responsible for ensuring that everyone understands the problem and is involved in its solution.

Role of the Teacher:

- Assign students to groups (see "Forming Groups") and explain student roles.

- Develop problems and projects that involve subtasks and that suggest student communication, interaction, and teamwork.

- Serve as a facilitator who encourages student involvement in the group.

- Monitor the progress of the group toward the project solution while observing that individual students are performing their tasks.

- Provide suggestions to the groups without providing solutions. Try to keep the students "on track" without determining the "track."

- Assess not only the final results but the efforts of the individual students. See *Scoring Rubric* sheet and *Self/Group Self-Assessment* sheet.

Forming Groups

Cooperative learning groups are usually groups of three to five students. Partners (groups of two) can also be assigned group work or projects. However, partner work would not offer the diverse interactions resulting from larger groups. Teachers can form groups by random or by assigning students based on ability levels, personalities, and behaviors.

Random assignment can be as easy as having students count off—all ones form a group, all twos form a group, and so on. Students could draw cards or slips of paper assigning them to a group. Random assignment is often used when a teacher has not had enough time to determine students' abilities or personalities. Teachers can observe randomly assigned groups to determine the natural leaders and followers.

Assigned groups can be either **heterogeneous** or **homogeneous**. Heterogeneous groups consist of students of varying characteristics: students of greater ability with students of lesser ability, students with outgoing personalities with students who tend to be introverted, and students of various ethnic or language backgrounds. Teachers should be careful not to categorize students. At times, lesser-ability students can offer more to a cooperative learning group than greater-ability students since they may see the situation differently. A greater-ability student may not want to help others succeed if he or she is accustomed to always having the higher grades. All students must be encouraged to be active participants in the group activity.

Homogeneous groups consist of students of similar abilities or personalities. Homogeneous grouping can be most effective when the groups are given various tasks. Groups of greater-ability students can use their strengths to come to some outstanding conclusions. Groups of lesser-ability students can allow some students to excel who are otherwise intimidated by the brighter students. Teachers need to monitor homogeneous groups to be certain students are working cooperatively.

Problems

Some students may be uncomfortable with cooperative learning groups. Some students will not actively participate either out of lack of confidence or laziness. They fear that their comments will be wrong. Unmotivated or "lazy" students know that some member of the group will take up the slack so the team will be successful. Other students will prefer to do the task on their own so they receive the grade they feel they deserve. Teachers should have the groups complete self-assessments of the progress the group as a whole is making and of the progress individual students are making.

Some groups may not know how to work together. The students may not know how to start either because the group does not have a leader or because too many students want to control the group. Teachers should offer some group communication suggestions. Some initial questions might include:

"What is the goal of the project?"
"What materials are needed to accomplish the task?"
"What are the steps needed to gather the information?"
"Can you restate the problem?"

Teachers need to define the roles of the students in the group, monitor the relationship among the students, and check that the students are making progress toward the solution of the problem. Group assignments should vary throughout the year.

Assessment

Grading cooperative learning group activities can be a tricky task. If individual grades are to be given, the teacher must consider the individual effort as well as the team results. Many students feel cheated when a group grade is given and they feel they contributed more than other students. Since the task is intended to be a group effort, a group grade could count two thirds of the final project grade with one third being an individual effort grade. An individual effort grade should be an effort grade and not a "quantity of work" grade. Since the team was responsible for assigning tasks to its members, the effort by the individual should be the main element of the individual grade. Grading elements should be explained to the students before the tasks are started.

For the teacher, cooperative learning group activities provide the opportunity for alternative assessment. Alternative assessment implies alternative grading methods. A scoring rubric should be developed and shared with the students. Students should know how their solutions will be graded prior to completion of the group work. See the *Scoring Rubric*.

FIELD TRIP LETTER

This sample letter can easily be adapted to meet any school or district requirements.

Dear Family:

Our mathematics class is preparing for a Math Field Trip to _____ _____ to complete math investigations in a different environment. The field trip will be on _____ from _____ to _____. The activity will give students the opportunity to use the math concepts studied in the classroom in real-world situations.

Students will work in groups to collect data, analyze and interpret the data, and draw conclusions to complete an investigation. The math concepts include data analysis, measurement, geometric concepts and properties, and consumerism. The investigations will foster the lifelong skills of cooperation, communication, and strategic planning. The culminating activity will be a presentation of the groups' results to the class.

The following materials will be used by the students: string, tape measures, stop watches, large protractors, calculators, graph paper, paper, and pencil. If you could provide any of the listed materials, please send them to the school.

Students will need to bring a lunch or money to purchase lunch in the food court. Students may want to bring a small amount of money to shop; they will be given a short period of time to do some shopping during the lunch break.

I feel this will be an informative and educational experience.

Sincerely,

_____

✂--

Please complete this portion and return to school by _____.

_____ has my permission to participate in the Math in the Mall Field Trip on _____.

I will _____ will not _____ be able to serve as a chaperone.

Parent/Guardian signature _____

Math in the Mall Letter

This sample letter can easily be adapted to meet any school or district requirements.

Dear Family:

Your child is beginning a project: Math in the Mall to complete math investigations in a different environment. The project assignments will be made on _____ with the project due on _____.
The activities will give students the opportunity to use the math concepts studied in the classroom in real-world situations.

Students will work in groups to collect data, analyze and interpret the data, and draw conclusions to complete an investigation. The math concepts include data analysis, measurement, geometric concepts and properties, and consumerism. The investigations will foster the lifelong skills of cooperation, communication, and strategic planning. The culminating activity will be a presentation of the groups' results to the class.

The following materials will be used by the students: string, tape measures, stop watches, large protractors, calculators, graph paper, paper, and pencil. If your child has difficulty obtaining materials for the project, please contact me.

I feel this will be an informative and educational experience.

Sincerely,

_____

✂--

Please complete this portion and return to school by _____.

I, _____, am aware of the Math in the Mall project due on
      Parent/Guardian

_____. I will encourage _____ to work
                               Student

with the other team members to complete the tasks and prepare a presentation.

Parent/Guardian signature _____

MATH IN THE MALL REPORT

Team:

_____

Activities:

Materials:

Explain the project activities.

Plan:

Define clearly each team member's task and how that member plans to accomplish those tasks.

1.

2.

3.

Implementing the Plan:

Methods of Data Collecting

1.

2.

3.

The Data

1.

2.

3.

Solutions and Conclusions:

Attach any Diagrams, Maps, Charts

1.

2.

3.

Additional Activities/Plan Revision

TOP TEN TIPS FOR COMPLETING A PROJECT

Discuss the following tips for completing a project with your classmates.

1. Complete each section of the reporting form.

2. Be certain that each member's participation in the project is listed and demonstrated.

3. Be creative when devising the procedure. Make the project a team effort.

4. List all materials that were used to measure objects and collect data.

5. Develop a time line of tasks needed to complete the project.

6. Explain methods used to measure and collect data.
   Remember: The procedures are as important as the results.

7. Draw and label diagrams and charts to report any collected data. Use additional sheets of paper.

8. Use mathematical terms when reporting the data and conclusions.

9. Use complete and concise sentences when stating conclusions.

10. Discuss your results and determine any revisions to your plan.

Scoring Rubric

A scoring rubric is a list of the criteria or standards used to evaluate a project. It is important to let students know what is expected. The "Project Scoring Rubric" should be shared with students prior to the project. The sample rubric is based on a 5-point scale for each component of the project, for a total of 35 points. The rubric should be adapted to meet the teacher's teaching and evaluation style.

Team:

5   Team members are listed. Each member was assigned well-defined tasks. Each member completed the specified task. The members worked well together.

4   Team members are listed. Team member tasks are listed. Most tasks were completed. The members worked together to complete the project.

3   Team members are listed. Team member assignments are not well-defined. Most tasks were completed. Some members of the team did most of the work.

2   Team members are listed. Member assignments are not specified. Some needed tasks were not completed. Several members did not complete their tasks.

1   Team members are listed. No additional information concerning the team is given.

Materials:

5   Materials list is complete.
4   Most materials are listed.
3   Some materials are listed.
2   Few materials are listed.
1   No materials list is given.

Explanation of Activities:

5 Written explanations show a clear understanding of the activities and needed information.

4 Written explanations show understanding of the activities and suggest needed information.

3 Written explanations show some understanding of what is required to complete the project activities.

2 Written explanations are rather brief and contain very little information as to what the activities entail.

1 Little or no explanation is given.

Plan:

5 The plan is complete with all members assigned tasks. The plan includes specific steps in a logical order.

4 The plan includes tasks for all group members. A list of tasks is included.

3 The plan is a general statement of the various tasks needed to complete the project. Member assignments are sketchy.

2 The plan is a brief statement of activities. No particular assignment of tasks is given.

1 The plan is not complete. Very little information is given.

Implementation of the Plan—Data:

5 Appropriate methods of data collection were used. Data items are complete and consistent for the activities. Appropriate units of measurement are used.

4 Appropriate methods of data collection were used. Some information or units of measure are missing or inaccurate.

3 Methods of data collection are not well-stated. Some data information is incorrect. Units of measurement are not consistent.

2 Methods used are not stated. Data inconsistent with the activities.

1 Methods are not stated. Data incorrect or missing.

Solutions/Conclusions:

5   Diagrams, maps, and charts are included and correctly labeled. Conclusions are reasonable and clearly stated.

4   Diagrams, maps, and charts are included. Conclusions are given.

3   Solutions are incomplete. Conclusions are appropriate for the solutions stated.

2   Solutions are incomplete. Some diagrams, maps, and charts are not included. Conclusions are incomplete.

1   Solutions are incomplete. Diagrams, maps, and charts are not included. Conclusions are vague and incorrect.

Additional Activities/Revisions:

5   Creative activities are suggested. Stated revisions to original plan are included.

4   Routine activities are suggested. Revisions are included.

3   Additional activities and revisions are very vague.

2   Additional activities or revisions are missing.

1   Additional activities and revisions are missing.

STUDENT SELF-ASSESSMENT

NAME: _____

OTHER TEAM MEMBERS: _____

_____

_____

_____

PROJECT ACTIVITIES: _____

_____

1. My participation in the project included _____

_____

2. The most interesting part of the project was _____

_____

3. The most difficult part of the project was _____

_____

4. The most surprising fact about the project was_____

_____

5. I wish I had known more about _____

_____before I started my part of the project.

6. In general, I thought the project was (check all that apply):

_____ easy	_____ very enjoyable	_____ very interesting
_____ medium difficulty	_____ enjoyable	_____ interesting
_____ difficult	_____ neutral	_____ not very interesting
_____ very difficult	_____ not enjoyable	_____ boring

7. If I were asked what grade I deserve for my participation in this project, I would give myself a grade of _____ because _____

_____

GROUP SELF-ASSESSMENT

TEAM MEMBERS: _____   _____

_____   _____

PROJECT ACTIVITIES: _____

_____

MEMBERS' ROLES: _____

_____

_____

_____

_____

1. The group did really well at _____

_____

2. The group had trouble with _____

_____

3. The group could have done better if _____

_____

4. The easiest part of the project was_____

_____

5. The most difficult part of the project was _____

_____

6. Check all that apply:

_____ The group worked well together.

_____ Each member did a fair share.

_____ The group came up with a good plan.

_____ The project was a success.

Comments: _____

_____

SUGGESTED ACTIVITIES/PROJECTS

The *Suggested Activities/Projects* can be used by individual students or small groups. These activities can be assigned as part of a mathematics field trip or as part of a long-term mathematics project. Teachers and students should read through the activity sheets prior to a field trip to determine any needed materials. It is assumed that students will have access to calculators and measuring tools. Additional activities are given in *Other Math Field Trips*. Activities in *Mall Math* can be used to review math concepts.

ACTIVITIES (math skills)	ACTIVITIES RELATED TO MALL MATH
ADVERTISING: SIGNS OF THE TIMES (logos, geometric shapes)	GEOMETRY ROUNDUP
ALL THAT GLITTERS . . . (comparative shopping, percent)	PERCENTS AT THE MALL
AT THE MOVIES (costs, percent, time)	AMUSEMENT PARK MATH, PERCENTS AT THE MALL, SYMBOLICALLY SPEAKING
THE BEST THE MALL HAS TO OFFER (better buys)	BETTER BUY: "BUYER BEWARE"
BUSY AS A BEE (data collecting/analysis)	DATA DIAGRAMS
COLLEGE COLLECTION (budget, costs)	AMUSEMENT PARK MATH
COVERED IN PATTERNS (transformations)	DATA DIAGRAMS
DEMOGRAPHIC DATA (data collecting/analysis)	SLIDE, FLIP, TURN
DRINK ORDER: WATER (data analysis, distance)	NOT ALL FEET ARE EQUAL
FOOD, GLORIOUS FOOD! (cost, percent, unit price)	AMUSEMENT PARK MATH, BETTER BUY: . . . , PERCENTS AT. . . , SYMBOLICALLY. . .
GAME PLAN (better buy, measurement)	BETTER BUY: . . . , A MODEL EXERCISE
GETTING FROM HERE TO THERE (symbolic notation)	SYMBOLICALLY SPEAKING
IT'S NOT THE SIZE OF THE GIFT THAT COUNTS (costs, unit price, volume)	BETTER BUY: "BUYER BEWARE"
KITCHEN KNOW-HOW (costs, measurement, scale drawing)	BETTER BUY: . . . , A MODEL EXERCISE

ADVERTISING: SIGNS OF THE TIMES

A. Draw nine store or brand name logos. Identify the geometric shapes used.

1.

2.

3.

4.

5.

6.

7.

8.

9.

B. On a separate sheet develop a matching game, matching the logos (without store or brand names) to the store or brand names.

C. Design a logo for a store you would want to open in the mall.

ALL THAT GLITTERS. . .

Visit a jewelry store to learn about carats (also karat).

GOLD: The purity of gold is given in *carats*. Eighteen-carat gold is 75% pure gold.

1. List other types of gold commonly used in jewelry. Determine the percents of purity.

   _____

   _____

2. What is "pure gold"?

   _____

   _____

3. Compare the prices of similar pieces of jewelry that are made from different types of gold. (High school class rings are often available in different metals.)

   _____

   _____

DIAMONDS: A *carat* is a unit of weight for precious stones.

4. A *carat* is one of the "4 Cs" used to describe a diamond. What are the other "Cs"?

   _____

   _____

   _____

5. How much does a *carat* weigh? _____

6. Compare the prices of similar pieces of jewelry that are made with different weights of diamonds. _____

   _____

7. What is the weight of the largest diamond in the store? _____
   What does the piece of jewelry cost?_____

AT THE MOVIES

Answer the following questions concerning movies shown at a theater.

1. How many different movies are shown? _____

2. How many movies are rated?
   G ____   PG ____   PG13 ____   R ____   Other ____

3. What percent of the movies are rated?
   G ____   PG ____   PG13 ____   R ____   Other ____

4. List the ticket prices:
   Children _____
   Adults   _____
   Special prices:

5. Is there a special matinee price? _____
   If yes, how much would your family save by going at the matinee time instead of
   the evening time?_____ # of adults _____ # of children _____

6. Each member of your family wants
   popcorn and a soft drink. What will your
   family buy and what will be the cost? Be
   certain to indicate the sizes of popcorn
   and soft drinks you will buy.

   _____
   _____
   _____
   _____

7. You arrive at the movie theater at 4 p.m.
   A. What is the first movie you can see? _____
   B. How long will you have to wait?_____
   C. How long is the movie in minutes? _____ in hours? _____
   D. When will the movie end? _____

The Best the Mall Has to Offer

Compare various prices at the mall and determine best buys.

BEST SALE:

Find the "Best Sale." _____

Explain why it is the "Best Sale."

_____

_____

_____

Give an example of the savings by shopping the "Best Sale."

_____

_____

_____

_____

BEST MEAL DEAL:

Find the "Best Meal Deal." _____

Explain why it is the "Best Meal Deal."

_____

_____

_____

Give an example of the savings by buying the "Best Meal Deal."

_____

_____

_____

_____

BUSY AS A BEE

Determine the "busiest store" and "busiest food place" in the mall.

1. What criteria was used to determine "busy"?

   _____

   _____

   _____

2. Was the criteria the same for the store as for the food place?

   _____

   _____

   _____

3. How was your data collected?

   _____

   _____

   _____

4. What day and time did you use for your study?

   _____

   _____

   _____

5. Do you think the data used would change for other days of the week?
   Other times of day?

   _____

   _____

   _____

6. The "busiest store" is _____.
   The "busiest food place" is _____.

COLLEGE COLLECTION

Assume you are going off to college and you have nothing for your dorm room. A desk, a chair, a bed, a chest of drawers, and a closet are the only furnishings. Decide what things you want to buy. Determine a budget. Search the mall for the best prices for what you want to buy. Decide which you really need and which you can do without.

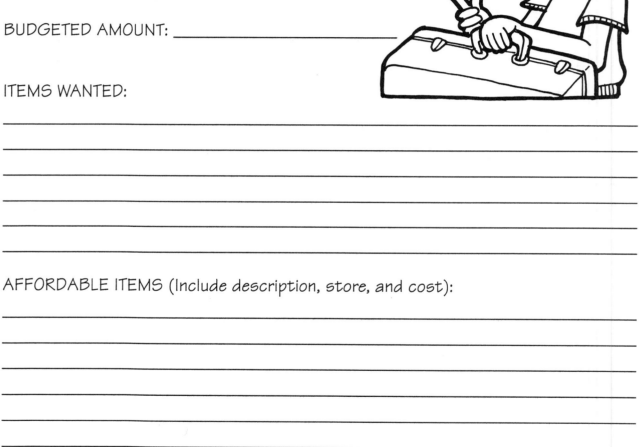

BUDGETED AMOUNT: _____

ITEMS WANTED:

_____

_____

_____

_____

_____

_____

AFFORDABLE ITEMS (Include description, store, and cost):

_____

_____

_____

_____

_____

_____

COVERED IN PATTERNS

Visit a Home Furnishings Department. Look at comforters and quilts.

Identify the patterns as slide, flip (reflection), or turn (rotation). Sketch three different designs below. Include one of each kind of pattern.

Design your own pattern for a comforter. Give your design a name and state whether it is a slide, flip (reflection), or turn (rotation).

STORE NAME: _____

Design Name: _____
Pattern Type: _____

Design Name: _____
Pattern Type: _____

Design Name: _____
Pattern Type: _____

YOUR DESIGN:

Design Name: _____
Pattern Type: _____

DEMOGRAPHIC DATA

Imagine that you have been hired to open a new store at the mall.

Advertisers and marketing executives collect information about their target population, location of the store, and their competition prior to manufacturing a new product or opening a new store.

Consider the following examples:

- A convenience store at an airport will probably sell more single-use (trial size) items than a neighborhood grocery store.

- In the northern hemisphere more swimsuits will be sold in May and June than in October and November.

Determine what demographic data is important for the success of your store. Consider age brackets, tourists vs. residents, existing stores, available local attractions (hobby items), etc.

Collect data concerning the shoppers at your mall—prospective shoppers at your new store.

State your results.

Based on your data, what type of store would you suggest? _____

DRINK ORDER: WATER

1. Draw a diagram of the mall and indicate the location of drinking fountains.

2. Determine the location of the water fountain that is used the most.

_____

_____

3. Calculate the distances between the drinking fountains and mark the distances on the sketch.

_____

_____

4. Decide on a location where an additional drinking fountain could be located.
   a. Describe the location. _____

   _____

   b. Give reasons for your choice of location. _____

   _____

   c. What are advantages/disadvantages of your location? _____

   _____

   Will it affect food court drink orders? _____

   Will it affect traffic in/out of stores? _____

FOOD, GLORIOUS FOOD!

1. Determine a menu for lunch and its cost.

   _____   _____

   _____   _____

   _____   _____

   _____   _____

2. How much would it cost if your entire family ate
   with you and ordered the same lunch? _____

3. How much would it cost for your class to eat this same lunch?   _____

4. Are there any foods, like pizza , that could be shared? _____

   _____

   _____

5. How many people could share a food and still have a good meal?   _____

6. How much money would be saved by sharing compared to each person buying a
   single serving?   _____

7. Is tax charged for food items? _____ If yes, what is the tax rate?_____

8. How much tax would be charged for #1? _____ #2? _____ #3? _____

9. Some establishments charge 15% gratuity for groups of six or more. If your class
   had to pay a 15% gratuity, how much would be added to the lunch cost?

   _____

10. Determine the cost per ounce for three different drink sizes.

    Size:_____   Cost: _____   Unit price:_____

    Size:_____   Cost: _____   Unit price:_____

    Size:_____   Cost: _____   Unit price:_____

11. Which is the "best buy" drink size? _____

GAME PLAN

Design your own game room. Visit furniture departments and electronic stores to find the best buys. List your needs, the stores where you could buy what you need, and the costs. Use the grid below to draw a diagram of the room to scale. Draw, cut out, and label shapes to represent the furniture. Make certain to include doors, windows, and any closet space.

SCALE: 1 cm = _____

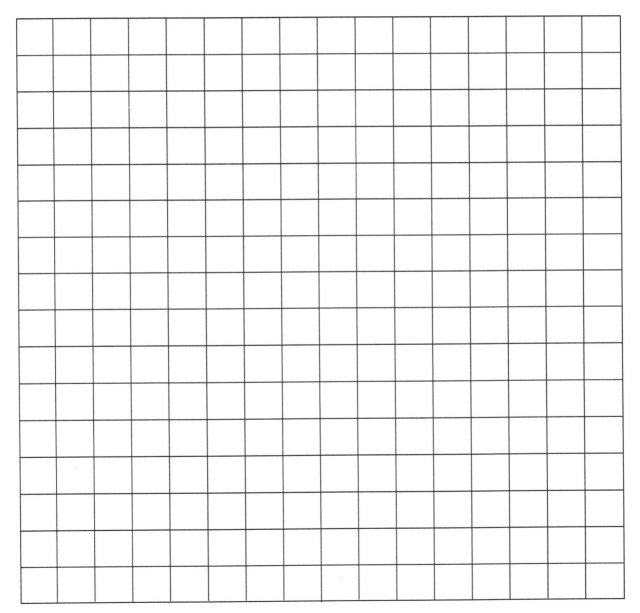

GETTING FROM HERE TO THERE

A set of directions to travel from one place to another can be written in words. It can also be shown symbolically.

Example:

These symbols might mean go east four stores, turn north two stores, and go up the stairs.

Use a set of symbols to give directions from one location in the mall to another location. Give your directions to your partner. Have your partner follow your directions and answer the questions below. Exchange roles and repeat the activity.

Your name: _____ Partner's name: _____

START:

Were the symbols understandable? _____

What changes would you suggest? _____

What was your final location? _____

Was it correct? _____

If not, what was the error? _____

START:

Were the symbols understandable? _____

What changes would you suggest? _____

What was your final location? _____

Was it correct? _____

If not, what was the error? _____

IT'S NOT THE SIZE OF THE GIFT THAT COUNTS

Visit a gift shop.

1. What is the largest item in the gift shop? _____

2. What is the smallest item in the gift shop? _____

3. How many of the smallest item could the largest item "contain"?_____
   Explain your method. _____

   _____

   _____

4. What is the most expensive item in the gift shop? _____
   Cost? _____

5. What is the least expensive item in the gift shop? _____
   Cost? _____

6. How many of the least expensive items could you buy instead of one of the most
   expensive items? _____

7. Find an item that is sold as part of a set;
   compare the cost of the set to the cost of
   purchasing each item separately.

   _____

8. What is the "best buy" in the gift shop?

   _____

   How did you determine the "best buy"? _____

   _____

   _____

KITCHEN KNOW-HOW

JOB: You have been hired to complete a kitchen. Use the diagram below (scale: 1 cm = 1 ft.) to design the kitchen. The kitchen has the indicated counters with a sink. Your budget is $5,000. Make certain the appliances will fit into the spaces. Accessorize the kitchen—it will need cookware, dishes, etc.

INVOICE: Make an invoice to present to your client. Be certain to include the suppliers (stores), item descriptions with appropriate dimensions, costs, etc.

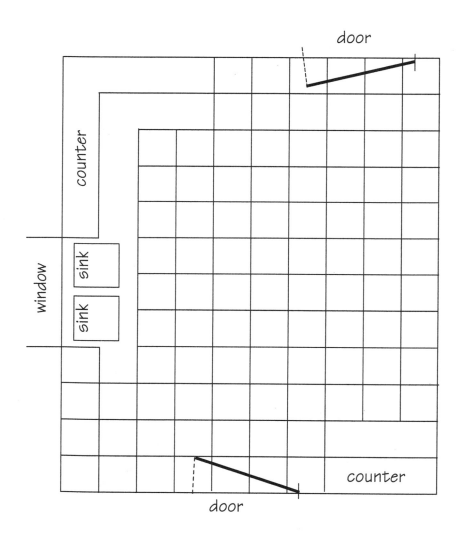

LINES, ANGLES, AND SHAPES, OH MY!

As you walk through the mall, find examples of each of the following. Define each shape, line, and angle; then draw a rough sketch and pinpoint its location. If needed, use additional sheets for diagrams.

LINES: perpendicular, parallel, skew

ANGLES: acute, right, obtuse, straight

SHAPES: prisms, pyramid, cone, cylinder, sphere

Name_____

MAKING MUSIC

Visit a music store that sells instruments.

1. List the major types of instruments sold.

_____
_____
_____
_____
_____

2. Complete the Venn diagram using the instruments from #1.

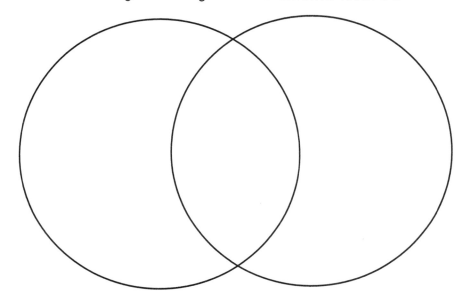

3. Choose an instrument. Compare the cost of buying, leasing, and renting the instrument.

_____
_____

4. What equipment (reed, strings, case, books, etc.) will be needed to play the instrument? _____
   Cost? _____

5. What is the "best buy" in the store? _____
   What percent savings is there? _____

MALL MAKEOVER

Imagine that you have been asked to renovate a wing of the mall using paint, tile, and carpeting.

1. Measure the length, width, and height of a wing of the mall.

   LENGTH: _____   WIDTH: _____   HEIGHT: _____

2. Explain methods used to measure the length, width, and height.

   _____

   _____

3. On the back of this page draw a diagram of the wing. Be certain to include doors, windows, etc. that will not be painted, tiled, or carpeted. Determine which sections will be painted, which will be tiled, and which will be carpeted. Calculate the areas. Label your diagram.

4. Research and record the cost and sources of paint, tiles, and carpet.

   PAINT: _____   _____

   TILES: _____   _____

   CARPET: _____   _____

5. Determine the amounts and costs of the materials for the renovation.

   PAINT: _____   _____

   TILES: _____   _____

   CARPET: _____   _____

6. TOTAL COST OF MATERIALS: _____

EXTRA: If the painters/installers charge $20/hr., estimate the labor costs. _____

MALL SIZE

Determine the size of the mall. Record your methods and results.

Use your pace as the unit of measure. Walk a distance counting your steps. Measure the same distance in feet or meters.

_____steps = _____ feet or meters

Sketch a floor plan (top view) of the mall:

Walk the mall. Convert your steps into feet or meters to determine the dimensions of the mall.

Calculate the area of the mall (show calculations).

_____

_____

Sketch a side view of the mall. Estimate the height(s) of the mall.

Calculate the volume of the mall (show calculations).

_____

_____

MALL WALKING

Determine appropriate paths of these three lengths for use by mall walkers—½ mile, 1 mile, and 2 miles. Do not include food court areas.

Walk a short distance counting the steps. Measure the distance in feet.

number of steps _____   distance _____

Use the distance as a unit of measure to determine the dimensions of the walkways of the mall. Explain the results. Use the grid below to make a scale drawing of the mall walkways. Indicate the location of major stores.

Scale: 1 cm = _____ ft.

Label the scale drawing to indicate the three mall walkers' paths. Indicate the number of times a path must be walked to complete the distances.

½ mile: _____   1 mile: _____   2 miles: _____

ONE OF A KIND

1. Visit a store that sells gifts that are unique to your area. Name of store: _____
   _____ What is the gift? _____

2. What makes the gift unique to your area?_____
   _____
   _____

3. What is the price of the "most unique" gift in the store? _____
   Item: _____
   What makes it the "most unique" gift?
   _____
   _____

4. What is the price of the most expensive gift in the store? _____
   What is it?_____

5. What is the price of the least expensive gift? _____
   What is it?_____

6. How many of the least expensive gifts could you buy instead of one of the most
   expensive ones? _____

7. Assume you are starting a store that specializes in products for the whole
   family.

What food item(s) would you sell? _____   Cost: _____

What movie(s) would you sell?_____   Cost: _____

What music CD(s) would you sell? _____   Cost: _____

What hobby/sporting item(s) would you sell? _____   Cost: _____

What type of clothing would you sell? _____   Cost: _____

What would you call your line of products? _____

PHOTOGRAPHIC GEOMETRY SAFARI

Go on a "Geometry Safari" armed with a camera. "Shoot" the following geometric shapes. For each geometric item, describe the object, give the location, and write the item number on your picture. (If possible, use a Polaroid camera so that you can see your results immediately.)

SHAPE:	OBJECT:	LOCATION:
1. square	_____	_____
2. rectangle (not square)	_____	_____
3. equilateral triangle	_____	_____
4. right isosceles triangle	_____	_____
5. hexagon	_____	_____
6. octagon	_____	_____
7. concentric circles	_____	_____
8. ellipse	_____	_____
9. parallel lines	_____	_____
10. parallel lines cut by a transversal	_____	_____
11. perpendicular lines	_____	_____
12. cylinder	_____	_____
13. cone or pyramid	_____	_____
14. reflection symmetry	_____	_____
15. rotation symmetry	_____	_____

A Picture Is Worth a Thousand Words

A *thematic plot* is a diagram in which products are labeled with symbols to indicate the type of product sold.

Develop a thematic plot of the types of stores in the mall. In the legend, give the symbol used for each type of location.

Legend	
Type	Symbol
Department Store	
Shoe Store	
Clothing Store	
Music Store	
Drug Store	
Card/Gift Shop	
Sports Store	
Grocery Store	
Restrooms	

Name _____

A Sea of Cars

Examine the parking lot and complete the following activities.
SAFETY NOTE: Use extreme caution when walking through parking areas.

1. Draw a diagram (to scale) of a section of the parking lot. Give the measurements of the angles and the lines.

2. Estimate the number of sections in the entire parking lot. _____

3. Estimate the total number of parking spaces. _____
   Explain your method of estimation. _____
   _____
   _____

4. Locate the handicap parking spaces. Give the measurements for the handicap
   spaces. _____

5. How much larger are the handicap spaces than the regular spaces? _____
   Explain. _____
   _____

6. Do you think the handicap spaces are large enough? Why or why not?
   _____
   _____

A Shoe of a Different Size

Visit a shoe store. Choose a brand of shoe that shows the shoe sizes for different countries, such as USA, UK, and EURO. Use another sheet of paper if necessary.

1. Give the brand and the shoe sizes.

2. Draw a diagram of the sole and label the following dimensions:
   (L) length
   (WB) width across the ball of the foot
   (WA) width across the arch
   (WH) width of the heel

3. Repeat #1 and #2
   for the same brand and style
   of shoe in a smaller size.

4. Repeat #1 and #2
   for the same brand and style
   of shoe in a larger size.

5. Choose a different brand.
   Use a similar style shoe in the
   same size as #1. Repeat #1 and #2.

6. Compare the measurements to the shoe sizes.
   A. What relationship exists between the length of a shoe and the shoe size?

   B. What relationship exists between the width of a shoe and the shoe size?

Name _____

THE SOUND OF MUSIC

Visit a music store.

1. List at least five categories of music sold by the store. For each category, estimate the percent of the store used to display the items.

   _____   _____

   _____   _____

   _____

2. Draw a diagram of the store floor plan and label the location of the categories.

3. What is the most expensive item in the store? _____ Cost? _____

4. What is the least expensive item in the store? _____ Cost? _____

5. What would you consider to be the "average" cost of a CD? _____

6. Choose a CD or a record that lists the lengths of the songs. List the songs and the stated times. Find the total time of the entire CD.

   _____ _____   _____ _____

   _____ _____   _____ _____

   _____ _____   _____ _____

   _____ _____   _____ _____

7. What is the best-selling type of music sold by the store? _____
   How did you determine your answer? _____

   _____

SUNDAE SURPRISE

Locate an ice cream shop that offers various syrups and toppings.

1. Total number of ice cream choices: _____
2. Number of ice cream choices that contain chocolate: _____
3. Number of ice cream choices that contain nuts: _____
4. Total number of syrups:_____
5. Number of syrups that contain chocolate: _____
6. Total number of toppings: _____
7. Number of toppings that contain chocolate: _____
8. Number of toppings that contain nuts: _____

Calculate the number of sundaes. Assume you may choose one ice cream flavor, one choice of syrup, and one topping. Show your calculations.

9. You like all types of ice cream, syrup, and toppings. How many choices do you have?

10. You are allergic to nuts. How many different sundae choices do you have?

11. You like everything with chocolate. How many different "all-chocolate" sundaes could you order?

12. You only like vanilla ice cream. You like all syrups and toppings. How many different sundaes could you make?

13. You only like sundaes with syrup, no other toppings. How many different sundaes could you order?

14. You only like chocolate syrup. How many different sundaes could you order?

15. If you ordered one sundae a day, how many weeks would pass before you would have to repeat an order?

16. On Sundays, you can order a two-topping sundae. How many different sundaes could you order? How many years would pass before you would have to repeat a Sunday sundae?

SURPRISE PARTY

Your class is planning a surprise birthday party for your teacher. Decide what party supplies (plates, napkins, etc.) and food items (pizza, cake, etc.) will be needed for each person. Calculate the quantity needed for the party.

Each Person	Entire Class

Comparative shop to find the best prices for the items. Remember, items sold in packages cannot be purchased individually.

Item	Store	Unit Price	Quantity	Cost

Total Cost of Party: _____

Cost per Student: _____

Name_____

SURVEYING THE STORES

Malls often have a Directory which lists stores under various categories, such as shoes, women's wear, music, etc. List six categories that would describe stores in the mall. List the stores in each category. Display your results in a circle graph. Calculate the percents and degree measurements.

Categories					
1.	2.	3.	4.	5.	6.
Stores					

Category: Percent: Degrees:

1. _____ _____ _____

2. _____ _____ _____

3. _____ _____ _____

4. _____ _____ _____

5. _____ _____ _____

6. _____ _____ _____

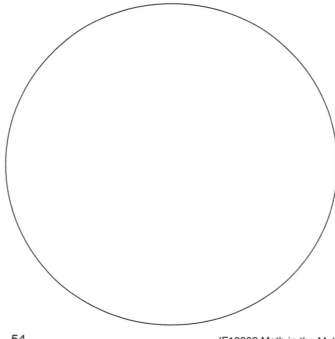

THROUGH THE EYES OF A MATHEMATICIAN

1. Describe the mall as a mathematician—use as many geometric terms as possible.

   _____
   _____
   _____
   _____

2. What streets form the "perimeter" of the mall?

   _____
   _____
   _____

3. Sketch two views of the mall.

   FRONT   SIDE

4. Is the mall symmetrical?
   If yes, what are the lines of symmetry?
   If no, why not?

   _____
   _____
   _____

5. When was the mall built? _____ How old is the mall? _____

UNREACHABLE HEIGHTS

To measure the height of a tall object, such as a flagpole or a building, one can use the sides and angles of a right triangle. A right isosceles triangle has two congruent legs and two 45° base angles. Your assignment is to estimate the height of an object at the mall using the following "homemade" clinometer.

Materials:
  large protractor
  drinking straw
  tape
  string
  washer or nut

Instrument (Clinometer):

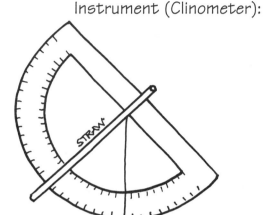

Figure 1

Walk far enough from the object so that you can see the top of the object through the straw (see figure 1) while the plumb line (string and weight) hangs vertically through 45°. Measure the distance between you and the object. That distance plus the height of your eye from the ground equals the height of the object. Refer to the diagram below.

Diagram:

Use the clinometer to measure the height of the mall flagpole. (If the mall does not have a flagpole, measure the height of the mall.) Be careful if you have to walk in a parking lot. Label the diagram below with your measurements.

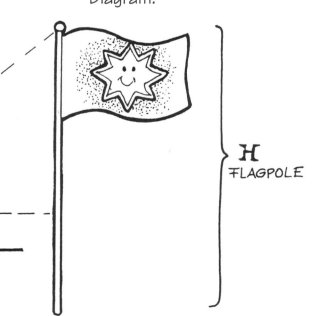

WATER, WATER, EVERYWHERE

1. Locate a decorative fountain in your mall. Describe the location of the fountain.

_____

_____

2. Draw a rough sketch of the fountain. Does it have any geometric shapes?

3. Measure the fountain.
   a. Describe the method you used.

   _____

   _____

   b. List the tools you used.

   _____

   _____

   c. Give the measurements.

   _____

   _____

4. Estimate the volume of the water in the fountain.

_____

5. Are there coins in the fountain?
   a. Estimate the amount of money in the fountain. _____
   b. Describe the method you used. Do not remove money from the fountain.

   _____

   _____

What Goes Up, Must Come Down

SAFETY NOTES: Use caution when near an escalator.
Be aware of any loose clothing and shoe strings.
Do not interfere with the operation of the escalator or block access to the escalator.

1. Locate an escalator. What is the angle of inclination? _____

2. How many "steps" are there on the escalator? _____
   Explain your reasoning. _____
   _____
   _____

3. What is the speed of the escalator in "steps per minute"? _____
   Explain your method. _____
   _____
   _____

4. Assume maximum capacity is one person (two persons for a double wide escalator) on every other step. What is the maximum capacity for the escalator?
   _____

5. Is the return escalator parallel to or crisscross to the escalator? _____

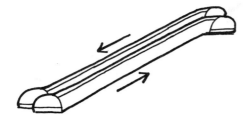 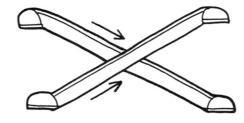

a. Explain the advantages and disadvantages of each style. _____
   _____
   _____

b. Which style is used more often at the mall? _____

WHAT'S IN A NAME

Find a grocery store or a drug store located in the mall you visit.

1. What is the name of the "store brand" of products? _____

2. Find ten national brand products that are available in the "store brand" family.

   On a separate sheet, state the following for each:
   • name and size
   • name of the national brand
   • cost—national brand and store brand
   • savings (or loss) by buying the store brand
   • percent of savings (or loss) by buying the store brand
   • width of the shelf display for the national brand and the store brand

3. What is the total amount saved if all ten "store brand" items are purchased rather than buying name brands? _____ Percent savings? _____

4. Were there differences in the shelf space given to the "store brands" versus the national name brand items? _____
   Conclusions? _____
   _____
   _____
   _____

5. Why would someone buy name brands instead of "store brands"?
   _____
   _____
   _____
   _____
   _____
   _____

THE WORLD OF SPORTS

Visit a sporting goods store.

1. What is the most popular sport in your area? _____

2. Is the popularity of the sport obvious when you walk into the store? _____
   Explain. _____
   _____

3. What is the most expensive piece of sporting equipment in the store? _____
   _____ Cost? _____ Sport? _____

4. By pricing the needed equipment and clothing, what appears to be the most
   expensive sport to play? _____
   List the equipment, clothing, and cost.
   _____ _____ _____
   _____ _____ _____
   _____ _____ _____

5. What is the most unique (different) product in the store? _____
   Explain. _____
   _____
   _____

6. Find something for sale that is sold as part of a set. _____
   Compare the cost of the set with the cost of purchasing each piece separately.
   Set _____
   Separate _____

7. Estimate the cost of buying one of each
   piece of equipment that pertains to your
   favorite sport (clothes, equipment,
   souvenirs, etc.). List them below.
   _____
   _____
   _____
   _____

You Are Here

Draw a diagram of the mall on the coordinate grid below.

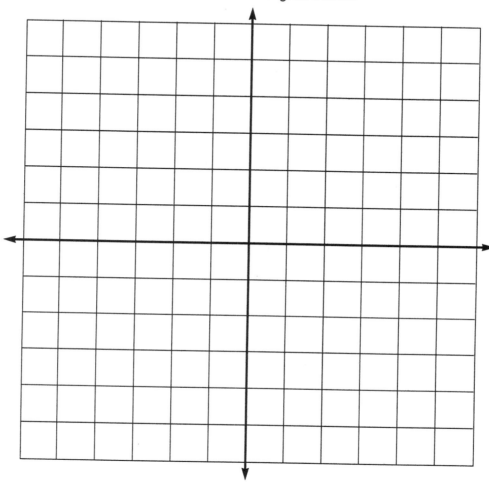

Give the coordinates for the following:
1. Main entrance (_____ , _____)
2. Customer Service/Information Counter (_____ , _____)
3. Fountain (_____ , _____) or other _____ at (_____ , _____)

Give the name and coordinates for each of the following:
4. Department store _____ at (_____ , _____)
5. Shoe store _____ at (_____ , _____)
6. Food store _____ at (_____ , _____)
7. Card/Gift store _____ at (_____ , _____)
8. Your favorite store _____ at (_____ , _____)

MALL MATH

Mall Math activities review math concepts the students may use to complete the activities in the *Suggested Activities/Project* section. It is recommended that the necessary activities be assigned and discussed prior to the Math in the Mall Field Trip or deadlines for the Math in the Mall Project.

ACTIVITIES	RELATED MATH CONCEPTS
AMUSEMENT PARK MATH	costs, percent, time, units conversion
AREA AND VOLUME	area, formulas, volume
BETTER BUY: "BUYER BEWARE"	unit price
CLEARING OUT THE CLEARANCE	discounts, percent
CURLY'S COMBINATIONS	combinations, data analysis
DATA DIAGRAMS	data analysis, Venn diagrams
DOUBLE TROUBLE	area, perimeter, volume
GEOMETRY ROUNDUP	geometric shapes and terms
A MODEL EXERCISE	ratio, scale factor
NOT ALL FEET ARE EQUAL	nonstandard units, units conversion
ONE VERSION OF CONVERSION	ratio, units conversion
PARTY TIME	costs, unit prices
PERCENTS AT THE MALL	percent
PERIMETER, AREA, VOLUME	use of perimeter, area, and volume
SHOWING OFF THE SHOP	area, costs, units conversion, view diagrams
SLIDE, FLIP, TURN	transformations
SYMBOLICALLY SPEAKING	circle graph, coordinate grid, percent, symbols

AMUSEMENT PARK MATH

1

The Slidewinder at Dollywood allows a maximum of five passengers and no more than 950 pounds on any one slide.

A. Would your family be able to ride together?

B. How many slides would be needed for your class?

2

The passengers on Daredevil Falls ride in an eight-passenger car. A car is released every 20 seconds. How long would it take for your class to be loaded?

4

A. A rate of $14.99/student and $24.99/adult is charged for your class for admission. What will be the total admission charge for your class and three chaperones?

B. The fee includes a lunch. Every student buys a drink for $.89. How much is spent on the drinks for all students?

C. A Gold Pass offers a 20% discount on food and merchandise. How much would you save on a $12.99 lunch bill and $23.95 souvenir bill?

3

A. The Dollywood Express train weighs 105 tons. How many pounds does it weigh?

B. On an average day, it uses three tons of coal. How many pounds of coal does it use?

C. On an average day, it uses 4,000 gallons of water. Water weighs approximately eight pounds/gallon. How many tons of water is used?

D. The train schedule starts at 11:00 a.m. The train leaves every hour with the last run at 5:00 p.m. The train can carry a maximum of 650 people. What is the maximum number of passengers in one day?

AREA AND VOLUME

Use the following formulas to find the area and volume of the given shapes.

Rectangle: Area = L x W   Triangle: Area= ½ B x H

Rectangular prism: Volume = L x W x H   Pyramid: Volume=(⅓) L x W x H

Divide each shape into rectangles, triangles, rectangular prisms, and pyramids. Find the area (or volume) of each part. Give the total area (volume) of the shape.

1. Area =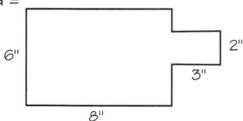

2. Area =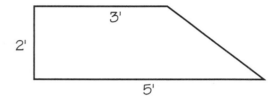

3. Area =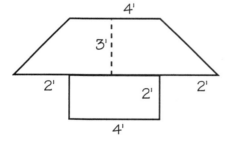

4. Volume =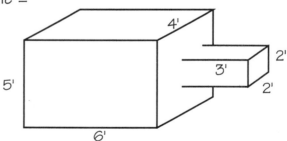

5. Volume =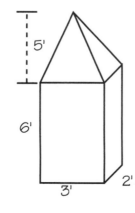

6. Volume =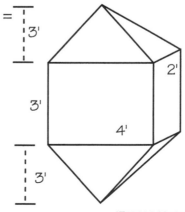

BETTER BUY: "BUYER BEWARE"

The "better buy" is when you pay the lower price per unit for a manufactured product. Usually the larger the container, the better the buy, but not always. Determine the "Better Buy" for each situation below. Divide the cost by the quantity in each container. Then compare costs.

①
Clean-It-Bright is available in two sizes.
The econo-size (32 oz.) costs $1.44.
The biggie size (48 oz.) costs $2.30.
Which is the better buy?
Econo-size: _____ per ounce

Biggie size: _____ per ounce

Better buy? _____

②
The 16-oz. size of Super-Cleaner is $1.20. The 30-oz. size is $2.16. Which is the better buy?
_____

③
Frosted Chips costs $3.25 for the 12-oz. size and comes with an instant 25¢ off coupon. The 20-oz. size costs $4.80. Which is the better buy? _____

④
Bobby's Better Beans come packaged 3 cans for $1.29 or 8 cans for $3.29.
Which is the better buy?
_____

⑤
Forever-Shine cleaner is on special. The 16-oz. size, regularly priced at $1.89, is a "buy-one, get-one free" special. The 30-oz. size, regularly $2.19, is 25% off. Which is the better buy?
_____

⑥
Pop-Easy Popcorn comes in two sizes. The small 20-oz. bag with 20% more free costs $0.84. The larger 40-oz. bag costs $1.39. Which is the better buy?
_____

CLEARING OUT THE CLEARANCE

Determine whether each statement is true or false. If false, give the reason.

1. Ali had the choice of buying two skirts 50%-off each or "Buy one, get one free." She told the clerk, it did not matter because the cost would be the same. _____

_____

_____

2. Jo found a bike at two different stores. At Mega-Mart, it cost $79 and had a $10 mail-in rebate. At Bob's Buyout, it was priced $75 with an additional 10% off. Jo bought the bike at Bob's Buyout to save money.

_____

_____

3. Sasha found a $90 coat on a 30%-off plus an additional 20%-off rack. She figured the sale price would be $45-50% of the original $90 price.

_____

_____

4. Juan bought a $100 table at a flea market at 20% off. He then sold it at a garage sale for 20% more than he had paid for it. Juan thought he would make $20 on the deal.

_____

_____

5. Kelli has an Advantage Card that gives a 10% discount on all purchases at Kate's Kwick Stop. The sales tax rate is 10%. So Kelli thinks the Card just covers the sales tax.

_____

_____

6. Mika was given two options for buying a $150 bike:
A—$50 down and 6 monthly payments of $20.
B—deferred payment for one year with a 20% finance charge.
Mika chose Plan A to save money.

_____

_____

7. Robert argued that an item on sale at 30% off plus an additional 20% off is a better deal than 20% off plus an additional 30% off since the larger percent would be subtracted first.

_____

_____

8. Jenny figured that 20% off plus an additional 20% off would be equal to 36% off since 20% off plus 20% is the same as paying 80% of 80% or 64%. Paying 64% is the same as 36% off.

_____

_____

CURLY'S COMBINATIONS

Curly's Cookie Shop lets customers decorate their own cookies with one flavor of icing and one topping.

Cookies	Icing	Toppings
sugar peanut butter chocolate	vanilla chocolate strawberry	sprinkles chocolate chips peanuts

Example: Katie does not like chocolate or strawberry. How many different cookies might she make?

$$\underline{\quad 2 \quad} \times \underline{\quad 1 \quad} \times \underline{\quad 2 \quad} = 4 \text{ combinations}$$
cookies   icing   toppings

Calculate the number of combinations.

1. Roberto is allergic to anything with peanuts. How many different cookies might he make?

2. Jenny likes all the choices. How many different combinations can she make?

3. Rashad does not want any topping, only icing. How many cookies will he make?

4. On Monday, Curly adds M & Ms to the list of toppings. How many different cookies can one make on Mondays?

5. Cal only wants a sugar cookie base. How many different combinations will he make?

BONUS: On Tuesdays, Curly lets customers use two toppings. How many different two-topping cookies can be made?
Hint: How many different pairs of toppings can be made from three toppings?

DATA DIAGRAMS

Venn diagrams are used to display data that may have common traits.

This Venn diagram shows the even, odd, and prime numbers 1 through 10. Since 2 is the only even prime, it is the only number in the overlapping region *even/prime*. Since 3, 5, and 7 are odd numbers and are also prime numbers, they appear in the overlapping region *odd/prime*. There are no numbers that are even/odd, and prime.

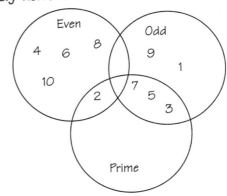

Complete each of the given Venn diagrams with the elements listed.

1. {5, 10, 15, 20, 25, 30}

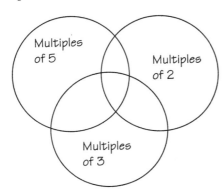

2. {chair, soil, cook, is, hat, write}

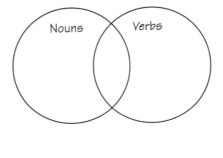

3. {2, 6, 9, 24, 27, 30, 32, 45}

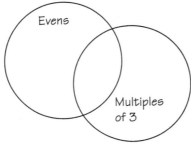

4. {-6, 0, 5, -23, 15, 21, -34}

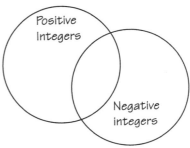

5. Draw and label a Venn diagram using {⅔, 5, 2.3, ½, 6⅓, 0, 83, 9}.

IF19302 Math in the Mall

DOUBLE TROUBLE

Use the following formulas.

Rectangle: Perimeter = 2 L + 2 W   Area = L x W

Rectangular prism: Volume = L x W x H

1. A garden measures 15' by 12'.
   A. How many feet of fencing are needed? _____

   B. If the length (15') of the garden is doubled, what is the "new" perimeter? _____

   C. If both dimensions of the original garden are doubled, what is the perimeter? _____

   D. How does C compare to A?
   _____

2. A carpet sample measures 6' by 5'.
   A. Find the area in sq. ft. _____

   B. If another sample has a length twice as long, what is the area?
   _____

   C. Another sample is twice as long and twice as wide as the first. What is the area of the sample?
   _____

   D. How does C compare to A?
   _____

3. A box measures 10" x 6" x 5".
   A. What is the volume of the box?
   _____

   B. Another box is twice as wide. What is the volume of the second box? _____

   C. A third box is twice as long, twice as wide, and twice as high as the first box. What is the volume of the third box?_____

   D. How does C compare to A?
   _____

4. A square 1" by 1" has an area of 1 sq. inch.
   A. What is the area of a square 2' by 2'?_____

   B. What is the area in square inches of a square 1' by 1'?_____

5. A cube 1" by 1" by 1" has a volume of 1 cu. in. What is the volume of a cube 2" x 2" x 2"? _____

GEOMETRY ROUNDUP

What does a Zoid hunter try to do?

Place the letter of the shapes above the corresponding number of the names.

1. Hexagon   A

2. Right isosceles triangle   D

3. Parallel lines cut by a transversal   E

4. Octagon   I

5. Perpendicular lines   O

6. Rhombus   P

7. Rectangle   R

8. Equilateral triangle   T

9. Obtuse triangle   Z

___ ___ ___ ___ ___ ___ ___ ___ ___
 2   6   1   5   9   4   8   3   7

A MODEL EXERCISE

Diagrams and models of objects are usually reduced versions of the original. The scale indicates the ratio of the model to the object.

EX: 1 in. = 5 ft. means each inch of the model represents 5 ft. of the actual object.

A model airplane with a wing measuring 4 in. means the actual plane has a 20 ft. (4 in. x 5 ft./in.) wing.

A 120 ft. building would have a model height of 24 in. (120 ft. x 1 in./5ft.)

Calculate the following model or actual object sizes based on the scales given.

1

Scale: 1 cm = 10 mi.
  A distance of 12 cm on a map is
    actually _____ miles.

  12 cm x _____ = _____ mi.

2

Scale: 1 in. = 6 ft.
  The model of a house measures 10
  in. by 15 in. The actual house is
  _____ ft. by _____ ft.

  10 in. x _____ = _____ ft.

  15 in. x _____ = _____ ft.

3

Scale: 1 cm = 5 m
  A 15-m tall structure would have a
  model height of _____ cm

  15 m x _____ = _____ cm

4

Scale: 1 in. = 25 mi.
  Oak Ridge is 375 mi. from Memphis.
  A map distance would be
  _____in.

  375 mi. x _____ = _____ in.

5

An 8" x 12" picture is to be enlarged
  150% (scale factor 1.5). The
  enlargement would measure
  _____ in. by _____ in.

  8 in. x _____ = _____ in.

  12 in. x _____ = _____ in.

6

A document 16" by 20" is to be
  reduced using a 75% setting (scale
  factor 0.75). The reduced page
  would measure _____ in. by
  _____ in.
  16 in. x _____ = _____ in.

  20 in. x _____ = _____ in.

7

Two triangles have the same shape.
  The base of the first is 3 in. and
  the height is 4 in. If the base of the
  second is 9 in., the height
  is_____ in.

8

8. What scale factor did you use in
  #7? _____

NOT ALL FEET ARE EQUAL

The unit of measure *foot* equals 12 inches. The *human foot* varies in length. If you know the length of your foot or your hand span, you can use the measurement to measure dimensions of objects when a ruler is not available. Measure the following in inches and in centimeters.

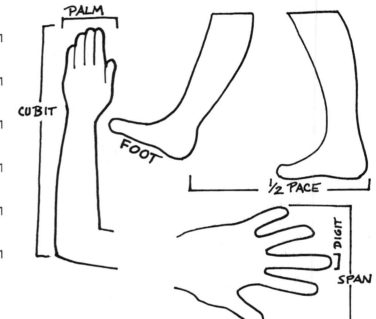

1. foot _____ in. _____ cm

2. span _____ in. _____ cm

3. palm _____ in. _____ cm

4. digit _____ in. _____ cm

5. cubit _____ in. _____ cm

6. ½ pace _____ in. _____ cm

Measure the following. Use the given "human unit of measure" and convert to inches.

7. desk top: length _____ spans _____ in.
                width _____ spans _____ in.

8. math book: length _____ palms _____ in.
                 width _____ palms _____ in.

9. doorway: _____ feet (your foot) _____ in.

10. length of hallway: _____ ½ paces _____ in.

ONE VERSION OF CONVERSION

To convert from one unit of measure to another, multiply by a measurement ratio equal to 1 so that you can cancel units. It is important to keep the units of measure when you write the measurement ratio.

Examples: 1 foot = 12 inches so $\dfrac{1\ foot}{12\ inches} = 1$ and $\dfrac{12\ inches}{1\ foot} = 1$

Change 42 in. to ft. $42\ in. \times \dfrac{1\ ft.}{12\ in.} = $ 7/2 ft. or 3.5 ft.

Change 5 ft. to in. $5\ ft. \times \dfrac{12\ in.}{1\ ft.} = $ 60 in.

Convert by using the correct measurement ratio so that the units will cancel.

1. Given 1 lb. = 16 oz., convert   a. 48 oz. x _____ = _____ lb.

   b. 7 lb. x _____ = _____ oz.

2. Given 3 teaspoons(t) = 1 tablespoon(T), convert   a. 6 T x _____ = _____ t

   b. 9 t x _____ = _____ T

3. Given 14 lbs. = 1 stone, convert   a. 35 lbs. x _____ = _____ stones

   b. 7 stones x _____ = _____ lbs.

4. Given 1 fathom = 6 ft., convert   a. 24 fathoms x _____ = _____ ft.

   b. 24 ft. x _____ = _____ fathoms

5. Given 1 cubit = 18 in., convert   a. 9 in. x _____ = _____ cubit

   b. 3 cubits x _____ = _____ in.

PARTY TIME

A class of 28 students is planning a surprise birthday party for the teacher. Calculate the total cost and the cost per student of the party.

Remember, items sold in packages cannot be purchased individually.

Polly's Party Supplies
plates	10 for $1.99
napkins	16 for $1.79
cups	10 for $1.79
forks	18 for $1.49

Mega-Mart
pizza	large (8 slices) for $10.99
apples	10/bag for $2.49
soda	12 cans for $2.99
cake	¼ sheet (16 servings) $10.99

For each person:
plate, napkin, cup, fork
1 slice of pizza
1 apple
1 can of soda
1 piece of cake

Calculate the quantity and total cost of each item:

1. plates _____ packages cost _____

2. napkins _____ packages cost _____

3. cups _____ packages cost _____

4. forks _____ packages cost _____

5. pizza _____ cost _____

6. apples _____ bags cost _____

7. soda _____ cans cost _____

8. cake _____ cost _____

9. total cost _____

10. cost per student _____

PERCENTS AT THE MALL

Percent means per hundred. The percent represents the number of hundredths when a ratio is written as a decimal ($\frac{3}{4}$ = 0.75 = 75%). Also, it equals the numerator of an equivalent fraction with a denominator of 100 ($\frac{3}{4}$ = $\frac{75}{100}$ = 75%).

Examples: An $80 coat is on sale for 25% off.
$\frac{25}{100}$ = D/80
$\frac{1}{4}$ = D/80
D = $20 discount

10 of the 15 racks contained women's shoes.
$\frac{10}{15}$ = P/100
$\frac{2}{3}$ = P/100
P = 66$\frac{2}{3}$%

Solve the following:

1. $\frac{4}{5}$ = _____%

2. 0.85 = _____%

3. 30% = _____ /10

4. 45% = _____/20

5. Ali could buy the CD on sale for $15 instead of $20. What percent of the original price is the sale price?

6. The $40 slacks were on sale for 15% off. How much would Tony save?

7. Only 1 rack of the 12 racks holds classical music CDs. What percent is classical music?

8. Rashad bought a gift for $29.95 plus 8% sales tax. How much tax was paid? _____
What was the total bill? _____

9. The Thomas family's dinner charge was $32.00. They plan to leave a 15% tip. How much was left for a tip?

10. A $120 jacket was sale-priced at $100. It was supposed to be 20% off. Was it correctly priced?

PERIMETER, AREA, VOLUME

For each situation, determine whether perimeter, area, or volume is the most appropriate measurement. Circle the answers in the tables below. Copy the circled letters above the problem numbers at the bottom of the page to complete a math fact.

1. framing a picture   perimeter (PER)   area (ITI)   volume (ARI)

2. filling a swimming pool   perimeter (MET)   area (UNI)   volume (IME)

3. spreading grass seed   perimeter (THE)   area (TER)   volume (IMA)

4. purchasing carpet   perimeter (OUT)   area (OFA)   volume (OIL)

5. edging a garden   perimeter (CIR)   area (CIL)   volume (CAT)

6. filling a gasoline tank   perimeter (ILO)   area (ALL)   volume (CLE)

7. air circulation   perimeter (IMA)   area (IRA)   volume (ISC)

8. painting a wall   perimeter (SEE)   area (IRC)   volume (DIN)

9. wallpaper border   perimeter (UMF)   area (LET)   volume (ALL)

10. ribbon for a package   perimeter (ERE)   area (TEA)   volume (IME)

11. wrapping paper for gift   perimeter (PIT)   area (NCE)   volume (GET)

8			11			9			10		
IRC	SEE	DIN	PIT	NCE	GET	ALL	UMF	LET	IME	TEA	ERE

3			6			2			5		
TER	THE	IMA	CLE	ALL	ILO	MET	UNI	IME	CAT	CIR	CIL

4			7			1		
OUT	OFA	OIL	IMA	IRA	ISC	PER	ARI	ITI

___ ___ ___ ___ ___ ___ ___ ___ ___ ___ ___
1   2   3   4   5   6   7   8   9   10   11

Name_____

SHOWING OFF THE SHOP

The Hi-Class Shop has been completed at the end of a wing of the mall. The area in front of the store needs a makeover. New tile flooring, carpeting, and paint will be needed. Use the information given to determine the quantity and cost of the materials.

The 30-ft.-wide and 15-ft.-high entry to the store (not part of the renovation) is located on a 60-ft.-wide wall at the end of the mall wing. The wing of the mall to be renovated is 120 ft. long with walls 20 ft. high. The walls are to be painted. The floor is to be tiled with 12" square tiles except for a small information center which is to be carpeted. The information center will measure 12' by 12' and will be located opposite the store entry at the opening into the main mall area. The ceiling is skylights and grillwork which will not be renovated.

On a separate piece of paper, make four diagrams with dimensions:
  1. end wall showing store entry
  2. one side wall
  3. other side wall
  4. floor showing information center

Calculate the following areas:

  5. wall area to be painted _____

  6. floor area to be tiled _____

  7. floor area to be carpeted _____

MATERIALS INFORMATION

PAINT	$12.99/gallon	covers 150 sq. ft./gallon
TILE	$.59/sq. ft.	45 tiles per box
CARPET	$14.99/sq. yd.	

Calculate the quantity and costs:

  8. paint _____ gallons   cost _____

  9. tiles _____ tiles   _____ packages   cost_____

  10. carpet _____ sq. ft.   _____ sq. yd.   cost_____

  11. total cost of materials _____

SLIDE, FLIP, TURN

One basic image can be used to make several different designs.

A **slide** is moving the image right, left, up, or down. Orientation does not change. Picture an arrow that points left. After a slide, the arrow still points left.

A **flip** (reflection) is flipping an image over a line of reflection. Left becomes right, or up becomes down. Picture an arrow that points left. After a flip over a vertical line, the arrow points to the right.

A **turn** (rotation) is moving the image around a point. After a 90° counterclockwise turn, left becomes down, up becomes left, etc. Picture an arrow that points left. After a 90° counterclockwise turn, the arrow points down.

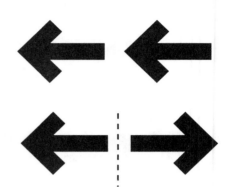

Make two different designs from the image below.

1. Slide

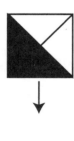

2. Flip

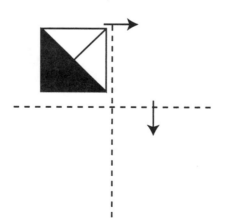

3. Turn

SYMBOLICALLY SPEAKING

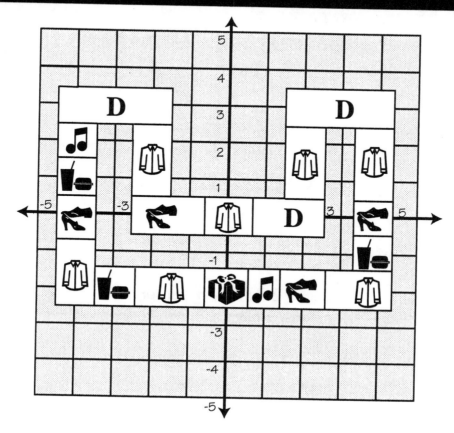

Refer to the thematic plot of Anytown Mall. Determine the number of each type of store. Compute the percents and draw a circle graph.

STORE:		NUMBER:	PERCENT:
1. Department	D	_____	_____
2. Clothing	👕	_____	_____
3. Gift/Card	🎁	_____	_____
4. Shoe	👠	_____	_____
5. Food	🥤	_____	_____
6. Music	♫	_____	_____

7. What type of store is located at (-4, 2)?_____

8. Give the coordinates for the gift store._____

OTHER MATH FIELD TRIPS

Several activities included in the *Suggested Activities/Projects* are also appropriate for a field trip to a museum or amusement park. Most of the geometry and measurement activities are applicable to museum settings. Some of the comparative shopping activities are appropriate for use in amusement parks and museums if they have a gift shop or a restaurant area. There are also a few extra activities in this section designed specifically for a trip to an amusement park or museum.

A teacher should

- visit the museum(s) or amusement park to make certain that the sites allow for the explorations and activities assigned.

- inform the museum or amusement park personnel of the field trip or the activities being assigned as projects. Educational information and special discounts may be available.

- review museum rules, such as taking photos, with students prior to the field trip.

- review specific safety rules for an amusement park.

The activities include the following:

Amazing Amusement Costs	Animal Sizes
Building Mathematics	From a Different Angle
Paintings	Playing the Games
Plotting the Park	Riding the Rides
Rocks and Minerals	Times Past

AMAZING AMUSEMENT COSTS

Find and compare the costs at the amusement park.

1. State the cost of entry to the amusement park for adults and children. Note the age bracket for children.

    ADULT: _____   CHILDREN (ages _____): _____

2. Are there any special rates for certain times, days, etc.?

3. Calculate the least expensive entry costs for your family or your class (including chaperones). Show your calculations. Include the times of arrival and departure.

4. How much was saved compared to what you would have spent at the most expensive times?

5. If rides are not included in the entry fees, determine an appropriate "Ride Package." List the types of rides and costs.

6. Consider the rides your family (or class members) would enjoy. What would be the cost of rides for your family (or class)?

7. Determine the cost of a basic lunch: sandwich or salad or pizza, chips or fries, and a drink. Calculate lunch costs for your family (or class).

8. What does your day at the park cost? _____

    What does a day cost for your family (or class)? _____

Name_____

ANIMAL SIZES

1. Locate an animal exhibit in the museum you visit. Name the animal._____

2. Determine the following measurements:
   A. Height _____

   B. Length of wing or front leg (arm)_____

   C. Length of back leg _____

   D. Length of tail _____

   E. Length of foot or paw or claw _____

3. What method did you use to determine the measurements?

4. Calculate the following animal ratios:
   A. Wing or front leg (arm) to height _____

   B. Back leg to height _____

   C. Tail to height _____

   D. Foot or paw or claw to wing or front leg (arm)_____

5. Determine the following lengths for an animal of the same species that is 5 feet tall:
   A. Length of wing or front leg (arm)_____

   B. Length of back leg _____

   C. Length of tail _____

   D. Length of foot or paw or claw _____

6. Calculate your arm-to-height ratio _____, leg-to-height ratio _____, and foot-to-leg ratio _____.

7. How do you compare to the animal you chose?

BUILDING MATHEMATICS

1. Describe the museum as though you were a mathematician—use as many geometry terms as possible.

2. What streets form the "perimeter" of the museum grounds?

3. Sketch two views of the building and label the dimensions.

FRONT VIEW	SIDE VIEW

4. If possible, locate the building cornerstone.
   In what year was the museum built? _____

5. How old is the building? _____

FROM A DIFFERENT ANGLE

1. Find an exhibit involving angles. Name of the exhibit: _____

2. Draw a diagram of the exhibit that shows the use of angles.

3. State the types of angles used and corresponding angle measures. _____
_____

4. Find another exhibit in which angles are used. Name of the exhibit: _____

5. Draw a diagram of the exhibit that shows the use of angles.

6. State the types of angles used and corresponding angle measures. _____
_____

PAINTINGS

1. Find one of the oldest paintings in the museum. _____

   A. Who was the artist? _____

   B. How old is the painting? _____

2. Choose an artist with several paintings on exhibit. _____
   Describe common features of the artist's work.

_____

_____

_____

3. Choose another artist with several paintings on exhibit. _____
   Compare the second artist's work to the first.

_____

_____

_____

4. How old were the artists when they completed the works on display?

_____   _____

5. A. Give the dimensions of a painting.

   Length: _____ Width: _____

   B. Give the width of the frame. _____

   C. Calculate the area of the painting. _____

   D. Calculate the wall area of the painting with the frame. _____

6. A. Double the dimensions of the painting. _____

   B. Calculate the "doubled painting's" area. _____

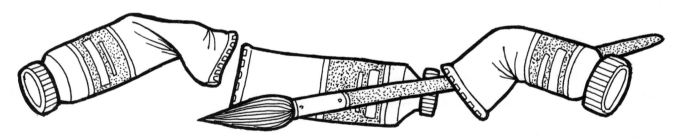

PLAYING THE GAMES

Locate a "skeeball-type" game. _____ Cost: _____

1. List the score/prize categories.

2. What is the average score per play for each prize category?

3. Suppose you have the lowest points on the first two balls. What must you score on the remaining balls to win any prize?   How can you score the needed points?

Choose another game of skill. _____ Cost: _____

1. Explain how someone wins a prize.

2. How many people played the game in 30 minutes? _____

3. How many people won a prize in 30 minutes? _____

4. What percent of the people won a prize? _____

5. Which game do you think you would have the greatest chance of winning a prize? _____ Why? _____

PLOTTING THE PARK

1. Survey the park. Determine five categories such as kiddie rides, games, food, etc. and create an appropriate symbol for each category.

	Category	Symbol
1	_____	_____
2	_____	_____
3	_____	_____
4	_____	_____
5	_____	_____

2. Draw an outline of the park on the centimeter grid given below. Use the symbols to " plot the park."

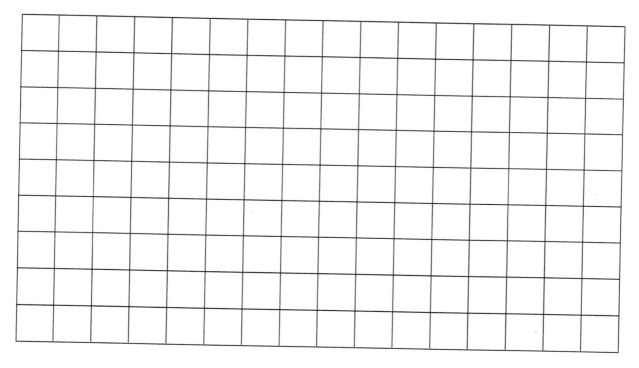

3. The given graph is a plot of speed versus time. Can you determine a ride that would match the graph?

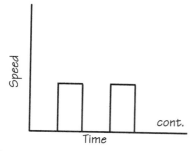

4. Choose another ride and graph the speed of the ride versus time. Name of ride: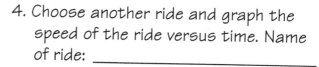

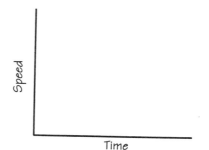

RIDING THE RIDES

1. Choose a ride. _____

2. Describe the ride. Include a description of the form of transportation.

   _____

   _____

For each of the following problems, explain the method used to determine the answer.

3. Determine the number of passengers allowed on the ride at any one time.

   _____

4. How long would it take for your class to ride the ride?

   _____

5. How many passengers can ride the ride in an hour?

   _____

6. Determine the time spent:
   A. waiting in line _____

   B. riding the ride _____

   C. What affects the answers to A and B?

   _____

   _____

   _____

7. Are there any restrictions on the passengers? _____
   Explain. _____

   _____

8. What would make the ride better? _____

   _____

ROCKS AND MINERALS

Locate a rocks and minerals exhibit in the museum you visit.

1. Approximate the number of rocks and minerals in the exhibit. _____

2. Method used to approximate the number:

3. Determine four categories for the elements of the exhibit. List at least three examples under each category.

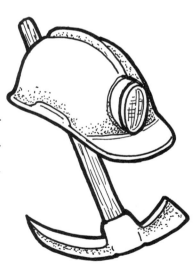

4. Locate the largest rock in the exhibit. _____
   A. Give its measurements. _____
   B. Calculate its volume. _____

5. Locate the smallest rock in the exhibit. _____
   A. Give its measurements. _____
   B. Calculate its volume. _____

6. How many of the smallest rocks would represent the same size as the large rock?

_____

TIMES PAST

1. Find the exhibit that houses the oldest artifact in the museum.

   Exhibit: _____ Date: _____

2. Calculate the age in years: _____ days: _____

   hours: _____ minutes: _____

   seconds: _____

3. Draw a time line starting from the date of the oldest item to the current year. Label the time line with ten events that are represented in the museum.

4. Find the oldest artifact pertaining to the United States exhibited in the museum.

   Item: _____ Date: _____ Age: _____

   Name the president at the time: _____

5. A president's term is four years.
   A. Determine how many presidential terms have occurred since the date of the oldest United States exhibit._____

   B. How many presidents have served since then? _____

Answer Key

Amusement Park Math   Page 63
1. A. varies
   B. varies
2. varies
3. A. 210,000 lbs.
   B. 6,000 lbs.
   C. 4,000 x 8 ÷ 2,000 = 16 tons
   D. 7 x 650 = 4,550 people
4. A. varies
   B. varies
   C. $7.39

Area and Volume   Page 64
1. 54 sq. in.
2. 8 sq. ft.
3. 26 sq. ft.
4. 132 cu. ft.
5. 46 cu. ft.
6. 40 cu. ft.

Better Buy: "Buyer Beware"   Page 65
1. Econo: $.045
   Biggie: $.048
   Econo
2. 30-oz. size
3. 20-oz. size
4. 8 cans
5. 30-oz. size
6. 40-oz. bag

Cleaning Out the Clearance   Page 66
1. true They are the same.
2. true Bob's is better buy.
3. false The coat would cost $50.40.
4. false $100 - 20% = $80
   $80 + 20% = $96
5. false Sales tax would be 10% of the discounted price.
6. true A—$170 B—$180
7. false They are the same.
8. true

Curly's Combinations   Page 67
1. 2 x 3 x 2 = 12
2. 3 x 3 x 3 = 27
3. 3 x 3 = 9
4. 3 x 3 x 4 = 36
5. 1 x 3 x 3 = 9
Bonus: 3 x 3 x 3 = 27

Data Diagrams   Page 68
1.

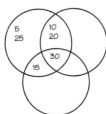

2.

3.

4.

5. Possible answer:

Double Trouble   Page 69
1. A. 54'
   B. 84'
   C. 108'
   D. twice as much
2. A. 30 sq. ft.
   B. 60 sq. ft.
   C. 120 sq. ft.
   D. 4 times as much
3. A. 300 cu. in.
   B. 600 cu. in.
   C. 2,400 cu. in.
   D. 8 times as much
4. A. 4 sq. in.
   B. 144 sq. in.
5. 8 cu. in.

Geometry Roundup   Page 70
1. A
2. T
3. I
4. Z
5. P
6. R
7. D
8. O
9. E
TRAPEZOID ("trap a zoid")

A Model Exercise   Page 71
1. 12 cm x 10 mi./1 cm = 120 mi.
2. 10 in. x 6 ft./1 in. = 60 ft.
   15 in. x 6 ft./1 in. = 90 ft.
3. 15 m x 1 cm/5 m = 3 cm
4. 375 mi. x 1 in./25 mi. = 15 in.
5. 8 in. x 1.5 = 12 in.
   12 in. x 1.5 = 18 in.
6. 16" x 0.75 = 12 in.
   20" x 0.75 = 15 in.
7. 4 in. x 9 in./3 in. = 12 in.
8. ⅔ or 3

Not All Feet Are Equal   Page 72
Answers will vary.

One Version of Conversion   Page 73
1. a. 48 oz. x 1 lb./16 oz. = 3 lb.
   b. 7 lb. x 16 oz./1 lb. = 112 oz.
2. a. 6 T x 3t/1 T = 18 t
   b. 9 t x 1T/3 t = 3T

3   a. 35 lbs. x 1 stone/14 lbs. = 2.5 stones
    b. 7 stones x 14 lb./1 stone = 98 lbs.
4. a. 24 fathoms x 6 ft./1 fathom = 144 ft.
    b. 24 ft. x 1 fathom/6 ft. = 4 fathoms
5. a. 9 in. x 1 cubits/18 in. = 0.5 cubit
    b. 3 cubits x 18 in/1 cubit = 54 in.

Party Time   Page 74
1. plates—3 packages = $5.97
2. napkins—2 packages = $3.58
3. cups—3 packages = $5.37
4. forks—2 packages = $2.98
5. pizza—4 = $43.96
6. apples—3 bags = $7.47
7. soda—36 cans = $8.97
8. cakes—2 = $21.98
9. total cost = $100.28
10. cost per student = $3.59
    since $3.58 is short $0.04

Percents at the Mall   Page 75
1. 80%   6. $6.00
2. 85   7. 8 1/3%
3. 3   8. $2.40; $32.35
4. 9   9. $4.80
5. 75%   10. no, 20% off is $96

Perimeter, Area, Volume   Page 76
1. perimeter   7. volume
2. volume   8. area
3. area   9. perimeter
4. area   10. perimeter
5. perimeter   11. area
6. volume

PER	IME	TER	OF A	CIR	CLE
1	2	3	4	5	6
IS C	IRC	UMF	ERE	NCE	
7	8	9	10	11	

Showing Off the Shop   Page 77
1.-4. check student drawings
5. end wall—750
   2 side walls—4,800
   total painted area = 5,550 sq. ft.
6. 7,200 - 144 = 7,056 sq. ft. of tiles
7. 144 sq. ft. of carpet
8. 37 gallons—$480.63
9. 7,056 tiles—157 packages—$4,168.35
10. 144 sq. ft.—16 sq. yd.—$239.84
11. total $4,888.82

Slide, Flip, Turn   Page 78
1.

2.

3.

Symbolically Speaking
1. 3   15%
2. 7   35%
3. 1   5%
4. 4   20%
5. 3   15%
6. 2   10%
7. music
8. (0, -2)

Page 79